scandia

LOM
ART

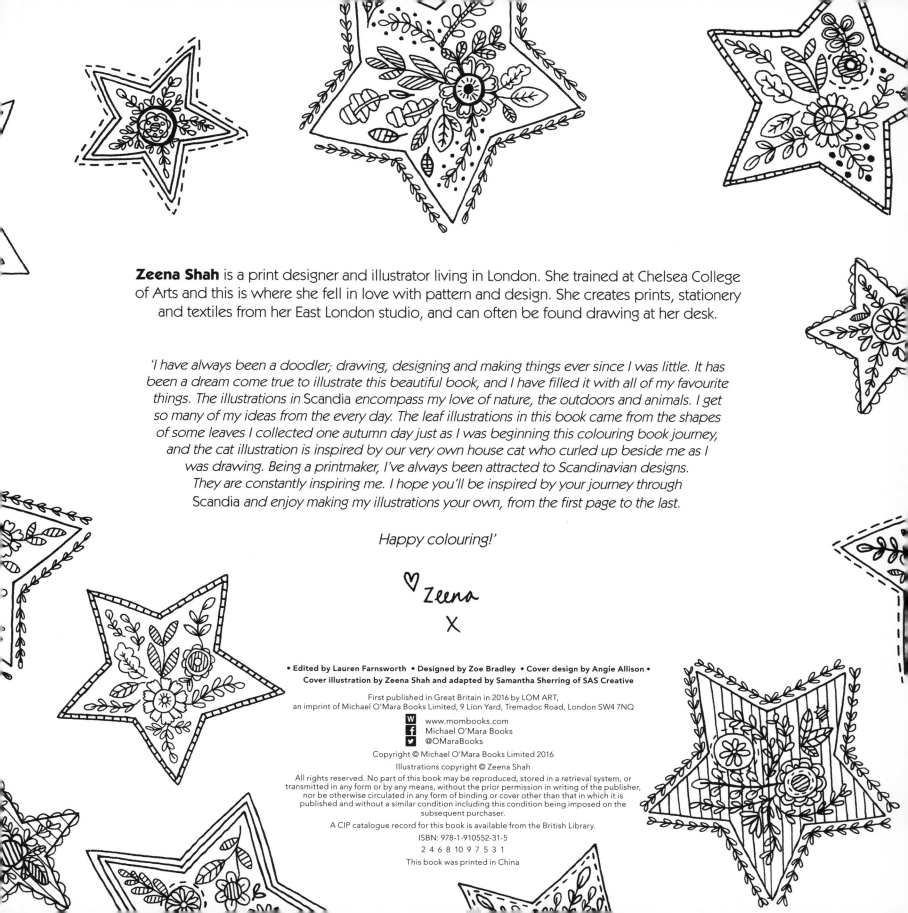

Zeena Shah is a print designer and illustrator living in London. She trained at Chelsea College of Arts and this is where she fell in love with pattern and design. She creates prints, stationery and textiles from her East London studio, and can often be found drawing at her desk.

'I have always been a doodler; drawing, designing and making things ever since I was little. It has been a dream come true to illustrate this beautiful book, and I have filled it with all of my favourite things. The illustrations in Scandia encompass my love of nature, the outdoors and animals. I get so many of my ideas from the every day. The leaf illustrations in this book came from the shapes of some leaves I collected one autumn day just as I was beginning this colouring book journey, and the cat illustration is inspired by our very own house cat who curled up beside me as I was drawing. Being a printmaker, I've always been attracted to Scandinavian designs. They are constantly inspiring me. I hope you'll be inspired by your journey through Scandia and enjoy making my illustrations your own, from the first page to the last.

Happy colouring!'

♡ *Zeena*
X

• Edited by Lauren Farnsworth • Designed by Zoe Bradley • Cover design by Angie Allison •
Cover illustration by Zeena Shah and adapted by Samantha Sherring of SAS Creative

First published in Great Britain in 2016 by LOM ART,
an imprint of Michael O'Mara Books Limited, 9 Lion Yard, Tremadoc Road, London SW4 7NQ

W www.mombooks.com
f Michael O'Mara Books
🐦 @OMaraBooks

Copyright © Michael O'Mara Books Limited 2016

Illustrations copyright © Zeena Shah

A CIP catalogue record for this book is available from the British Library.

ISBN: 978-1-910552-31-5

2 4 6 8 10 9 7 5 3 1

This book was printed in China

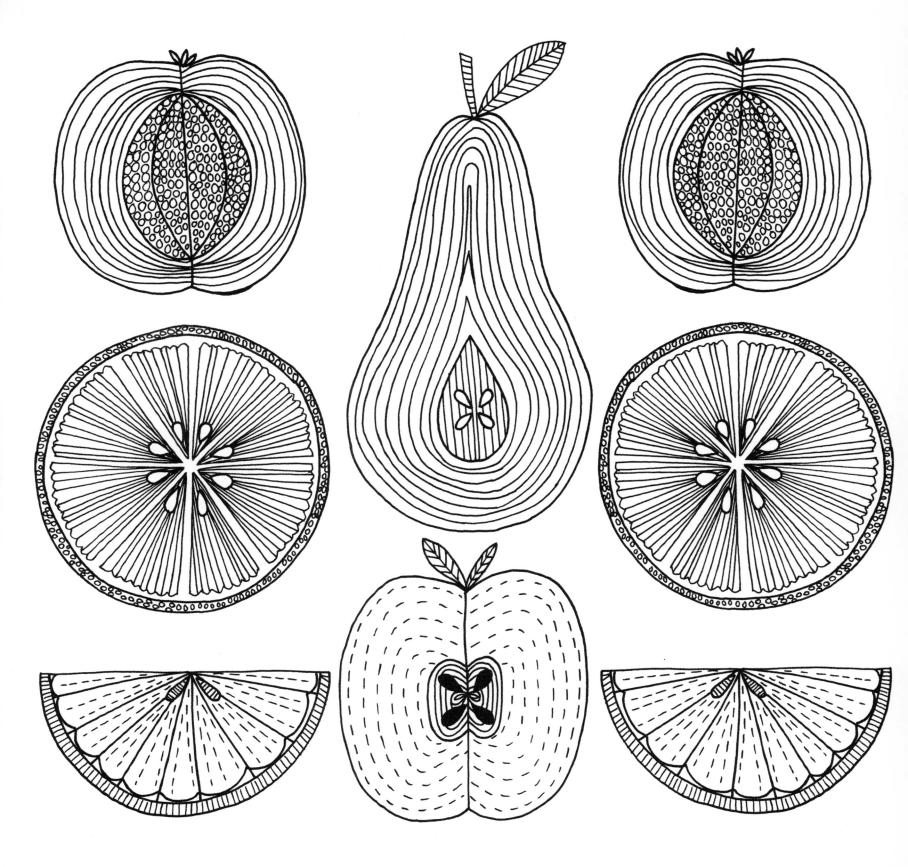

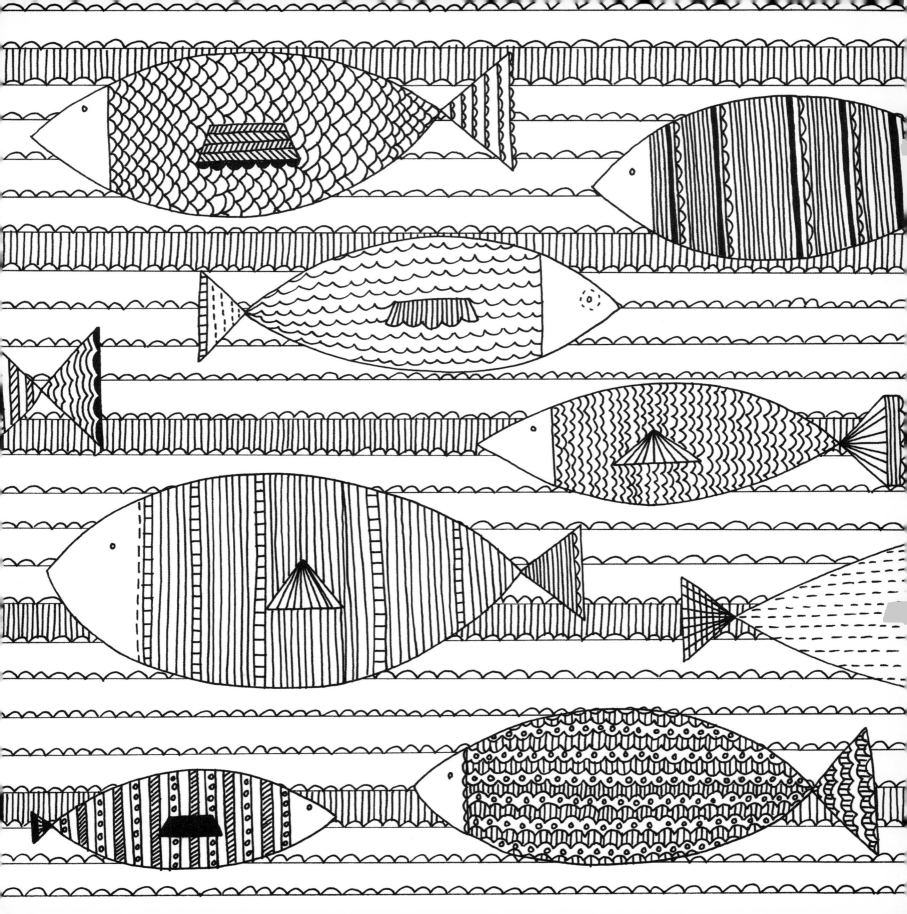

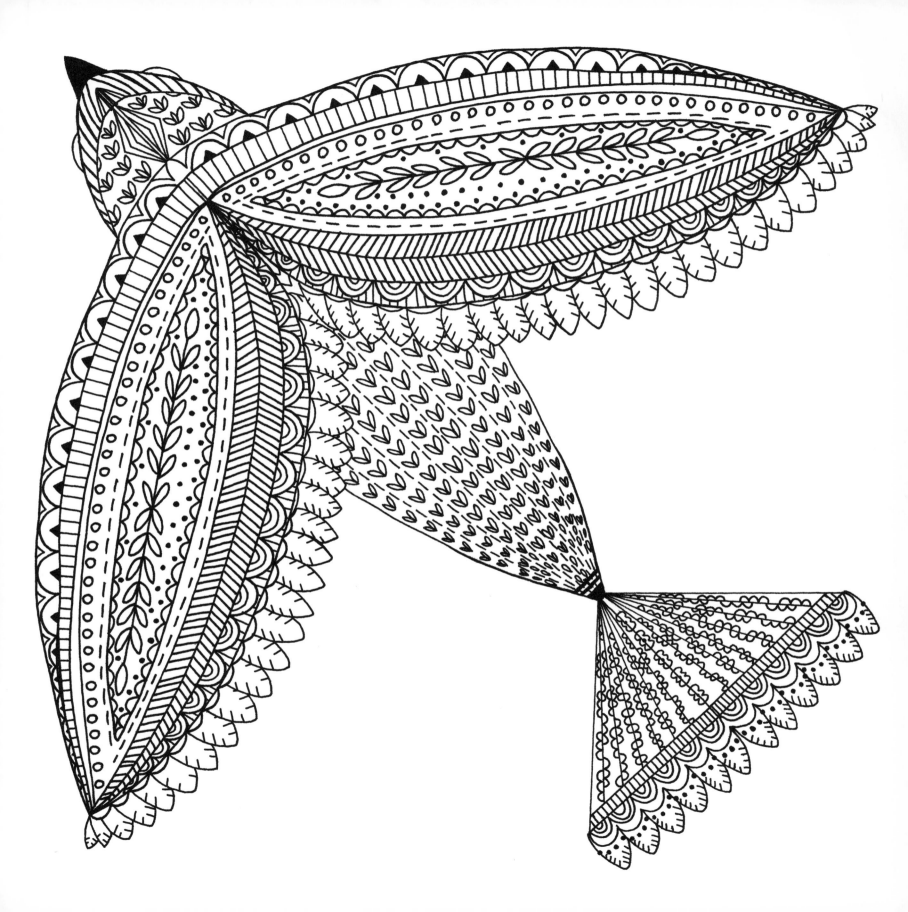